GW00375009

BOOK ONE

TAKE UP THE TRUMPET

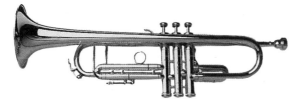

BY BRAM WIGGINS

CHESTER MUSIC

(A division of Music Sales Limited)
8/9 Frith Street, London W1V 5TZ.

Exclusive distributors:
Music Sales Limited
Newmarket Road, Bury St. Edmunds,
Suffolk IP33 3YB.

This book © Copyright 1992 by
Chester Music
Order No. CH60180
ISBN 0-7119-2970-X

Music processed by MSS Studios
King Silver 'Flair' trumpet courtesy of
Bill Lewington, Shaftesbury Avenue, London WC2H 8HN

Printed in the United Kingdom by
Caligraving Limited, Thetford, Norfolk.

TO THE STUDENT

You already know many of the tunes in this book and you will soon be able to play them all!

Do not worry if you cannot read music because, almost without knowing it, you will build up the skill as you enjoy working through the book. The **Note Recognition Games** and **Rhythm Practices** are fun to try and they will tell you how well you are doing.

Action Replays put the spotlight on potential problems. *Play these very slowly over and over again;* your fingers will quickly learn what to do and you will then be able to play them at the normal speed.

You will get a lot of fun from using this book, but remember that playing the trumpet is a serious business too. *Practise regularly and carefully follow the instructions of your teacher.* By doing this your playing will steadily improve and you will be able to perform even more of your favourite music.

TO THE TEACHER

The repertoire in **TAKE UP THE TRUMPET** has been most carefully chosen. Each tune has a specific teaching function: it may introduce a new note or rhythm, give practice over awkward fingerings, or perhaps promote good tone production, general control and finger dexterity.

Sometimes the explanation of a new notational element is deliberately left until it has been used several times in really well known melodies. The student's aural awareness will initially carry him or her through rhythmic problems; consolidation through theory and exercises comes later.

The graded **Note Recognition Games** and **Rhythm Practices** are designed to help with note reading; there are also plenty of less familiar and original pieces for sight reading.

TAKE UP THE TRUMPET is more than a 'fun' book. It provides a sympathetically structured background to each student's natural enthusiasm.

FIRST SOUNDS

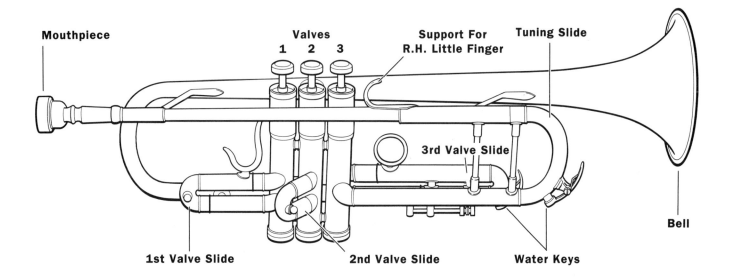

Mouthpiece | Valves 1 2 3 | Support For R.H. Little Finger | Tuning Slide | Bell | 3rd Valve Slide | 1st Valve Slide | 2nd Valve Slide | Water Keys

The Trumpet is basically a brass tube.

At one end it has a **mouthpiece** and the other end flares out - this end is known as the **bell** because of its shape.

Try blowing into the mouthpiece to see if you can produce any sounds; at the moment do not press any of the **valves** which you see in the middle of the tube.

You'll be lucky if you have produced any sound at all, let alone a real trumpet sound!

Never mind; let's now learn how to produce a good sound.

Try the following without using the instrument:

1. Tuck your lips in as if you are going to hum, or say the word "mum".
2. Keep as little of your lips showing as possible (look in a mirror to see if you think your lips look right).
3. Hold your lips tightly together and force air through them to produce a "buzz".
4. Then draw your lips together and see if you can produce a "buzz" which sounds higher.

Now take the mouthpiece only, place it in the *centre* of your lips and repeat the above exercises several times. It may not be a particularly pleasant noise, but should be nearer to the sound of the Trumpet.

Next, put the mouthpiece into the Trumpet and try the exercises again. You should now be producing a more attractive sound.

* Take all the weight of the Trumpet with your *left hand*. Your left thumb should be around the valve casing nearest to the mouthpiece, and your fingers around the furthest valve casing.

* Make sure that you hold the valves *upright*, not at an angle.

* Keep the mouthpiece in the centre of your lips.

* Blow just hard enough to make a pleasing sound.

* Make sure that you are not blowing your cheeks out.

* Your *right hand* will work the valves. Put your thumb *between* the first valve and the mouthpiece, under the mouthpipe, and your little finger in the ring or hook near to the bell. Your other three fingers should now sit comfortably on the three valve caps.

* Always take a deep breath before starting a note. Fill your lungs completely, using the muscle at the bottom of your lungs to control your breathing. This muscle is called the **diaphragm**.

* Keep your arms away from your sides so that you can breathe freely. Look in a mirror to see if your position is like the picture below.

* Your forearms should form an equilateral triangle (if you don't know what that is, ask your Maths teacher!). This is the most comfortable playing position and it makes it easier to breathe freely.

* Keep practising the first exercises, and see how many different notes you can play without pressing any of the valves.

Your notes should now be responding quite nicely, but you may have realised that they don't always sound *immediately*.

* You must now try to start them by placing your tongue behind your top teeth and imagine saying the syllable 'tu'; this action is called **tonguing**, and it is *most* important that you *start* every note in this way.

" Try a few notes tonguing very hard - i.e. emphasizing the 't' of 'tu'.

STAGE 1

The lowest note that can be played on the Trumpet *without* the valves is called **C** and it is quite likely that you have already been playing it, or possibly a higher one called

G *

For the moment let's concentrate on **(C)** . The best way to make sure that you are playing the correct note is to test it against the keyboard equivalent:

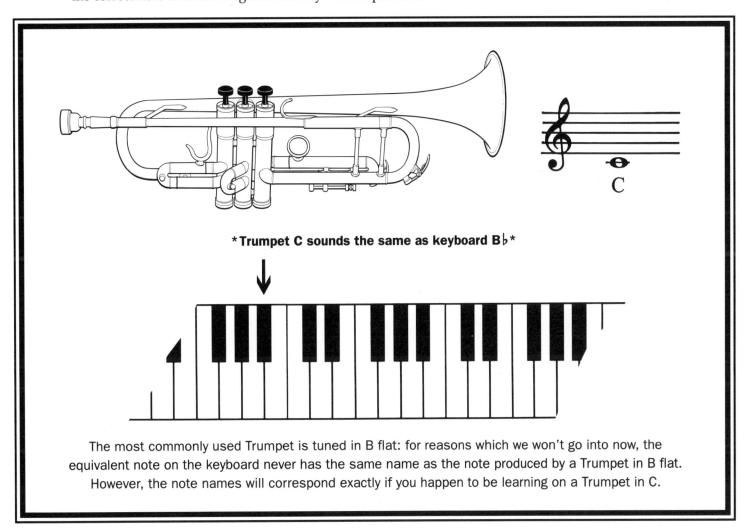

Trumpet C sounds the same as keyboard B♭

The most commonly used Trumpet is tuned in B flat: for reasons which we won't go into now, the equivalent note on the keyboard never has the same name as the note produced by a Trumpet in B flat. However, the note names will correspond exactly if you happen to be learning on a Trumpet in C.

Footnote:

*It may be that you find some difficulty in relaxing the lip enough to produce C, but the G above comes quite strongly. If so, try playing the following exercise, gradually relaxing as you go down. Don't be tempted to blow too hard. Once you get down to C, repeat the note a number of times so as to establish it. When you have got used to it, start going *up* again. Try to hold each note for a slow count of '1 2 3 4'.

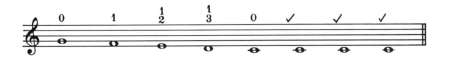

4

Listen and copy what your teacher plays:

Are you remembering to *tongue* every note?

Now, carry on playing the same note while your teacher plays some tunes to fit with it - before you start, count '**1 2 3 4**':

C IT MY WAY
B.W.

C ABOUT IT
B.W.

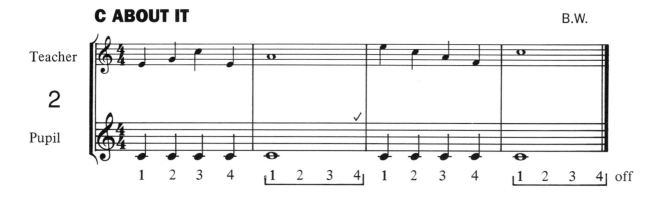

PASTORAL SYMPHONY FROM THE MESSIAH
G.F. Handel (1685-1759)

BAGPIPES
Czech traditional

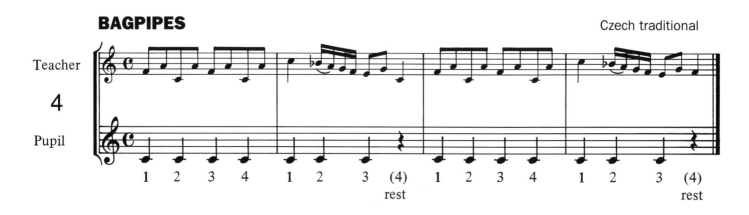

I AM SURE THAT YOU MUST BE WANTING TO TRY A FEW NOTES USING THE VALVES...

The note above  **(C)** is **(D)**

We play **(D)** with Valves 1 & 3.

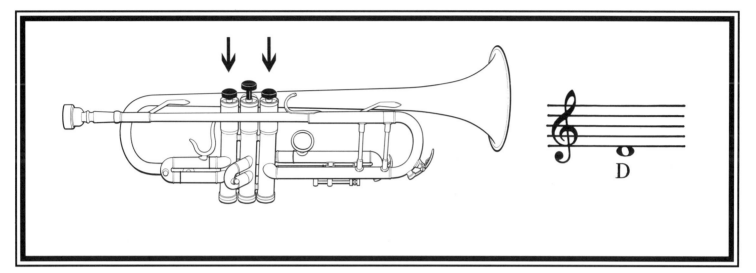

Play it, making sure that it is just *one step higher*. Remember to tongue.

Now let's go up another step to **(E)**

This note is played with Valves 1 & 2.

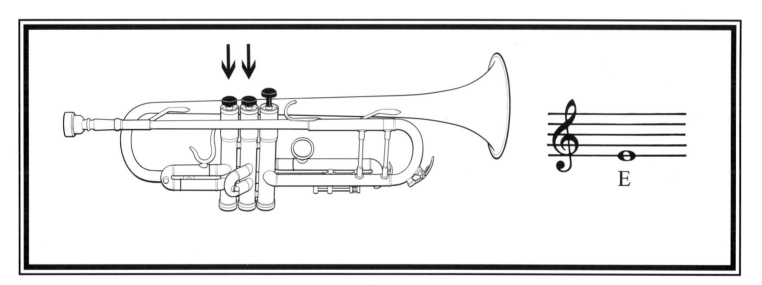

See if you can remember which valves to use for C, D and E, and play the following tunes. Hold the white notes while you count '1, 2, 3, 4' and count just '1' on the black notes:

Now try two tunes which you will know. They use your first three notes:

AU CLAIR DE LA LUNE

French traditional

Repeat sign, go back
and play it again

MERRILY WE ROLL ALONG

English traditional

The ticks (✓) show you where to breathe. The repeat signs (:‖) tell you to go back to the beginning and play the piece again. Let's have a little fun. See what those tunes sound like if you turn them upside down:

AU CLAIR UPSIDE DOWN

French traditional

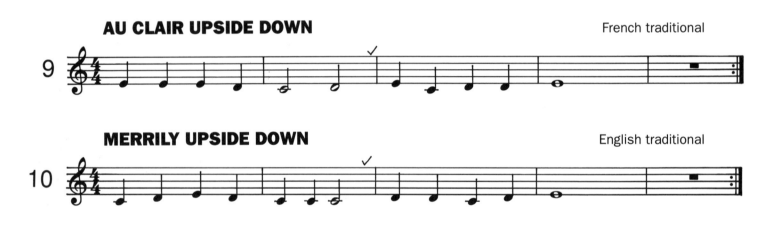

MERRILY UPSIDE DOWN

English traditional

The round white notes (**o**) which you have been playing are called **semibreves** (or **whole-notes**), and you must hold them for *four* counts (or beats) each.

The black notes with stems (♩ or ♪) are called **crotchets** (or **quarter-notes**). They are a bit quicker and last for just *one* count each.

You will have noticed some white notes with stems (♩ or ♪): these are called **minims** (or **half-notes**), and you must hold them for *two* counts each.

Try this tune:

FURRY FOLK TUNE

B.W.

STAGE 2

Your three notes 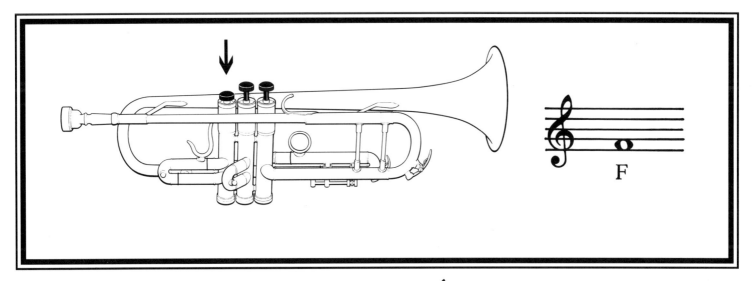 are probably quite strong now, so now's the time to move *up* to two new ones:

F is played with Valve 1 on its own:

G we have already met, and you will remember that, like you don't use any valves at all:

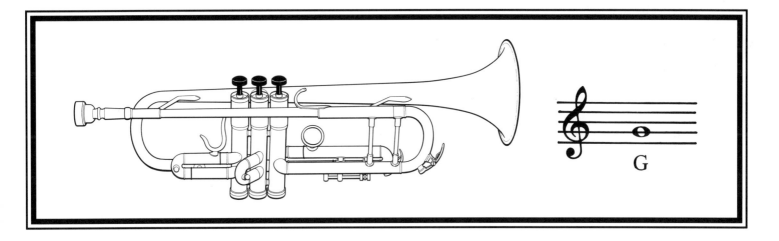

Let's move up to them by step:

FOUR GO IT

(o rest = 4 beats silence)

B.W.

1

Repeat sign: go back and play it again

FIVE ALIVE

B.W.

2

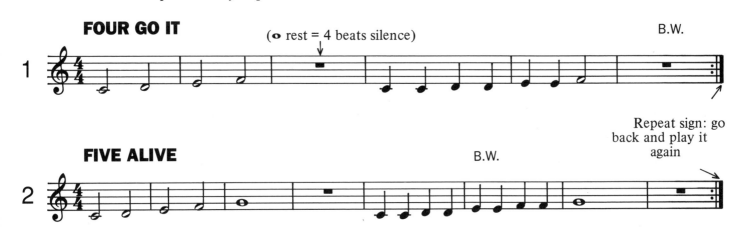

Introducing the **Note Recognition Game**:

Get someone to time you: first of all **naming** the notes, and then **playing** them.*

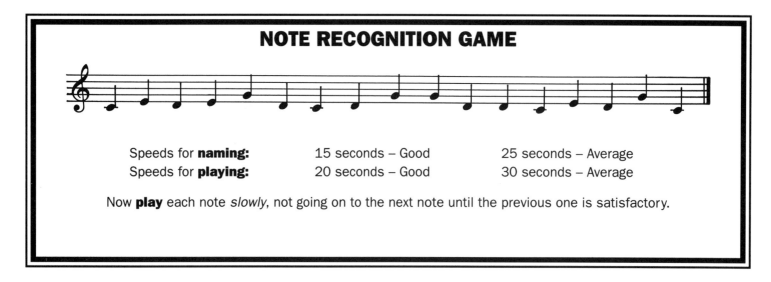

NOTE RECOGNITION GAME

| Speeds for **naming:** | 15 seconds – Good | 25 seconds – Average |
| Speeds for **playing:** | 20 seconds – Good | 30 seconds – Average |

Now **play** each note *slowly*, not going on to the next note until the previous one is satisfactory.

Footnote:
* (For the teacher). Playing notes as fast as possible is very rarely a good idea.
However, the **Note Recognition Games** work wonders in improving reading ability. Any harm done will be more than compensated for, if the pupil then (as instructed) plays each note of the Game slowly.

Here are some tunes using your first five notes:

ODE TO JOY (FROM SYMPHONY NO. 9) — L. Van Beethoven (1770-1827)

NOW THE DAY IS OVER (AN EVENING HYMN) — S. Baring-Gould (1834-1924)

WHEN THE SAINTS GO MARCHING IN — American traditional

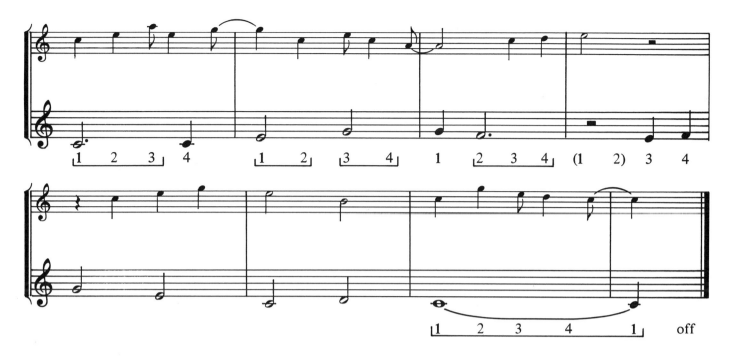

In *When The Saints* you will have noticed some more new signs.

(𝄽) is a **crotchet rest** (or **quarter-note rest**) -
i.e. silence for *one* count.

(▬) is a **minim rest** (or **half-note rest**) -
i.e. silence for *two* counts.

Count these rests as carefully as you would count the notes.

One of the (♩) s in this tune has a dot after it: this makes it sound a bit
longer - *three* counts. A (♩.) is called a **dotted minim** (or **dotted half-note**).

The curved line between the last two notes is called a **tie**. It joins together
two notes *on the same line* (or *in the same space*) to create a longer sound -
five counts in this particular tune.

It is very important that you play long-note studies - each practice session should begin and end
with a few long notes. This develops your sound and breathing. Start each note using your tongue
correctly, and finish it cleanly by just stopping your breath. Always feel that you are *blowing through
the tube, not into it*. Think of the sound getting to the furthest wall. *Count carefully* and *listen*. This is
an example of what to do:

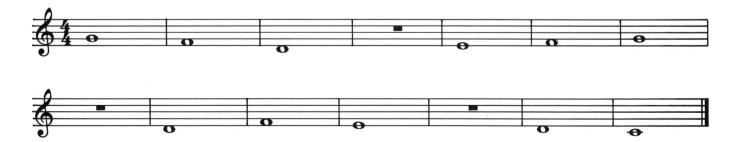

You can make up your own by simply changing the order of the notes!

Try reading the next three tunes - you won't know them, because they have been written for this book!

FIVER

B.W.

PENTATHLON

B.W.

FIVE-A-SIDE

B.W.

No.9 is a little German tune. It is arranged as a duet so that your teacher (or a friend) can play some faster notes with you. Practise your part on your own so that you know it quite well before trying to play it together. Remember to *count your beats carefully,* or you will find it difficult to keep together!

SUMM, SUMM, SUMM

German traditional

STAGE 3

Your teacher has the tune in the next piece - I'm sure you know it! Soon you'll know enough notes to be able to play the whole tune yourself! For now, practise the notes that have been written to fit with it. When you know your part well enough, try it with your teacher. The tune moves more quickly, so count the beats very carefully, and listen. You *should* end up together on the same note!

EASTENDERS THEME

Osbourne & May

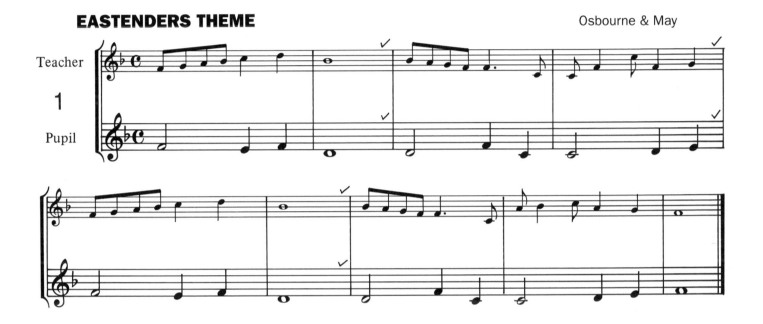

So far, all the tunes that you have played have been organized into groups of four (♩) counts, divided by vertical lines. These lines are called **bar-lines**, dividing the music up into equal **bars**. You will have noticed the figures at the beginning of each tune (4/4) : the *top* figure tells you *how many counts there are in each bar*, and the *bottom* figure is a *code to tell you the type of notes to count* - in this case (♩) s (crotchets or *quarter*-notes).

Now let's look at some tunes in (3/4) - three (♩)s in each bar. Waltzes are always in (3/4) time; the next tune is part of a very famous waltz:

BLUE DANUBE

J. Strauss II (1825-1899)

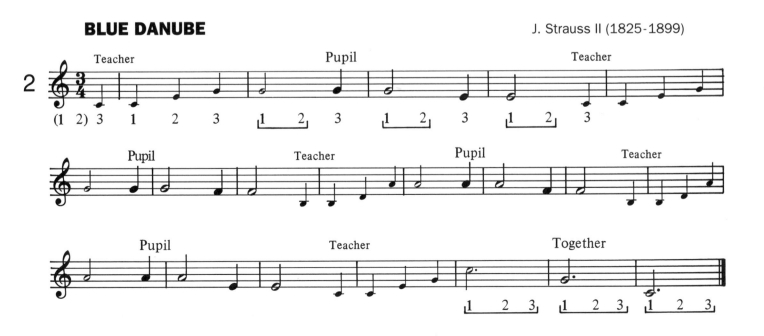

12

This is part of a tune from another Strauss waltz. It is not quite so famous as the *Blue Danube*, but can often be heard at concerts of Viennese music:

ROSES FROM THE SOUTH   J. Strauss II (1825-1899)

and the start of a not so familiar waltz by Schubert:

WALTZ   Franz Schubert (1797-1828)

Always remember to breathe in the right places. Music usually falls into short sections (**phrases**): get into the habit of breathing between each section, rather than breaking up the flow of the music by breathing in the middle of a phrase.

See if you can read these three unfamiliar tunes in ¾ :

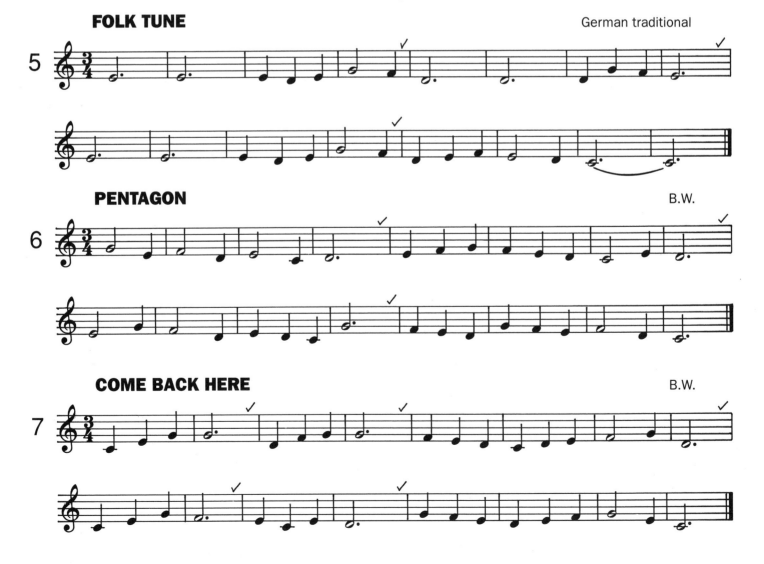

FOLK TUNE   German traditional

PENTAGON   B.W.

COME BACK HERE   B.W.

The distance between one note and a higher one is called an **interval**. C to E is the interval of a **third** - this is so called because you include both notes and any which have been missed out in between. So the intervals D to F and E to G are also thirds: in each case one note is missed out.

Try this:

GEORGE THE THIRD

B.W.

The interval from C to F is a **fourth**; so is D to G :

GEORGE THE FOURTH

B.W.

C to G is a **fifth**:

GEORGE THE FIFTH

B.W.

These are the notes you have learnt so far:

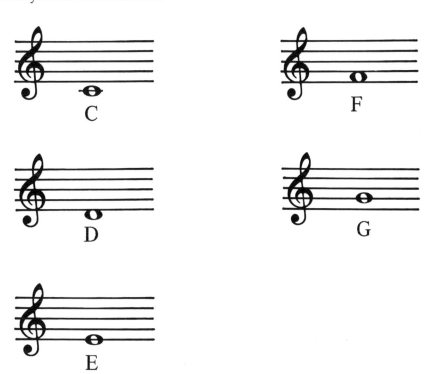

CHECKPOINT

If you have been having trouble with any of the tunes you have been playing, go through this check-list:

1. Are you holding your instrument correctly, with your left hand taking *all* the weight? Are the valves as *upright* as they should be, and are the *tips* of right hand fingers on the valve caps?

2. Make sure that when you move more than one valve they move *together* and *quickly*.

3. Are you remembering to *tongue* each note separately?

4. Are you breathing *deeply*?

5. Are you *counting* carefully, giving each note and rest the right length?

6. Always *listen* to make sure you are making a pleasant sound. Try to include some *long* notes every time you practise: this will help you with your breathing as well as improve the sound you're making.

7. Are you practising *regularly*? Remember that it's much better to do 15 minutes every day than one or two long, exhausting sessions a week!

8. Are you sure that you are not blowing out your cheeks? *Do keep them in*!

You should by now be having fun with your trumpet. See if you can make up some tunes of your own, using your first five notes. If you experiment with the valves, you may find that you can play some notes in between these five notes that you haven't learnt yet!

Don't hurry through the book. If you make sure that you really know each new note, and can play each tune thoroughly before moving on, you'll soon be able to play more interesting tunes.

STAGE 4

The next new note is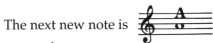

Like **E** you play it with the Valves 1 & 2, but you must draw your lips *a little tighter*

together to produce this higher note:

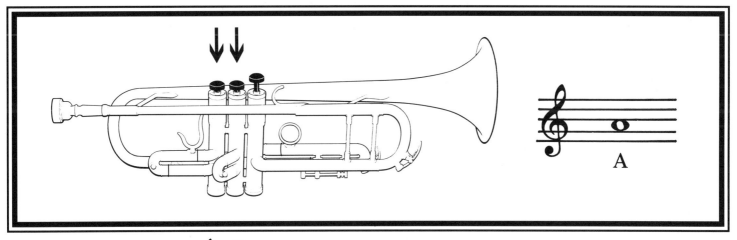

Up one more step to **B** For B you use the Valve 2 on its own:

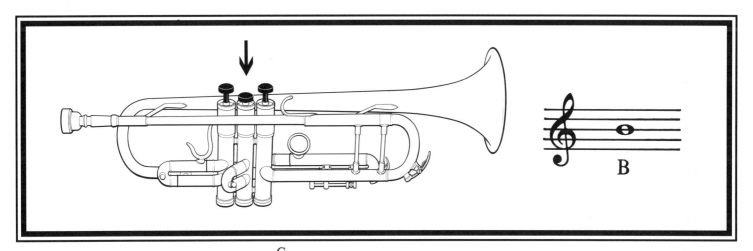

And now up to another C, **C** higher than the first note you learnt.

Like the lower C (**C**) you don't use any valves at all:

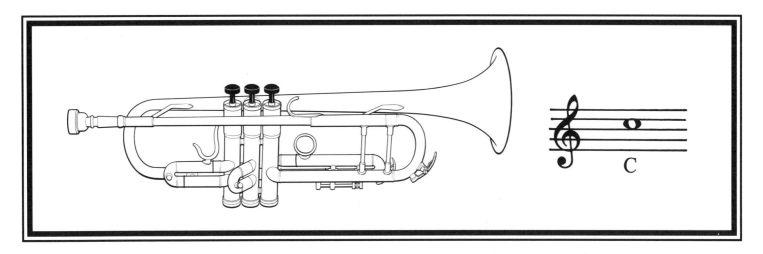

You can now play three notes without valves - **Low C**, **G** and **High C**.

You must draw your lips closer together as you go up.

See if you can play these three notes without touching the valves:

You may recognize that little phrase (especially if your teacher adds the two notes at the end!): it starts the music used for the TV Space Programmes and is also featured in the film, **2001, A Space Odyssey**. Its real title is **Also Sprach Zarathustra**, a piece for orchestra by Richard Strauss.

Play these three short pieces to practise moving gradually up to your new notes:

GOING GAGA

B.W.

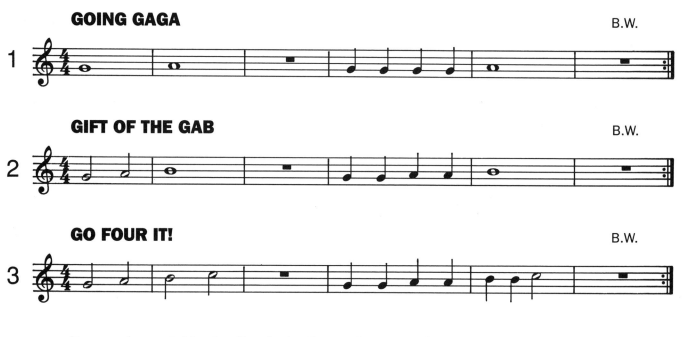

GIFT OF THE GAB

B.W.

GO FOUR IT!

B.W.

You now know eight notes. Try playing them going up step by step:

This series of notes is called a **scale**, and as it starts on **C**, we call it the **C scale**. (The word 'scale' comes from the Italian word 'scala', meaning a ladder or flight of stairs).

See if you can also play it backwards, coming down:

Scales are the framework on which most tunes are built.

Here's an old friend, *Au clair de la lune* (By the light of the moon). You can now play it complete:

AU CLAIR DE LA LUNE

French traditional

Did you notice anything else different? The moon has risen! - the tune began and ended on **F**, rather than **C**. When the *same* tune starts on a *different* note we say that it is in a different key.

Now here is a collection of tunes for you to play; they all use just eight different notes, the ones from the **C** scale:

VILLIKINS AND HIS DINAH/SWEET BETSY FROM PIKE English Music Hall Song

In the U.S.A. this song is called Sweet Betsy from Pike.

You have just played four tunes which may have been familiar to you - your ears should have told you if you played a wrong note!

Now see if you can *read* the next two - you won't know how they should sound, because they have been made up specially!

PIECES OF EIGHT
B.W.

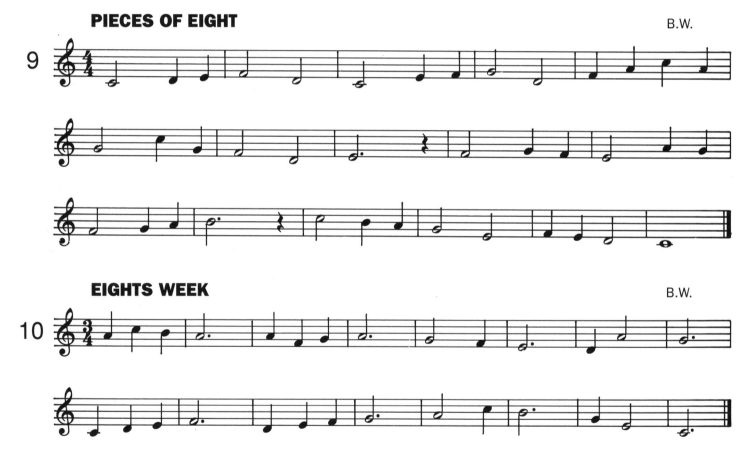

EIGHTS WEEK
B.W.

Here are two little **duets** (pieces for two players), which you can try with a friend, or perhaps your teacher will play them with you:

GO FOURTH
B.W.

COME FIFTH

B.W.

12

Why have these last two tunes been given these particular titles? (Hint: look carefully at how the notes jump up and down).

Now here's a tune from London which you may know. Keep your part going while your partner plays the quicker notes that have been added. Once again it would be best to practise your tune on your own before trying to play together.

ST. PAUL'S STEEPLE

English traditional

13

Did you notice how much of your C scale was used in that tune?

STAGE 5

Now try this well-known tune:

JINGLE BELLS

J. Pierpoint

1 & 2   3 & 4   1 & 2 & 3   (4)

You will have noticed that you played some quicker notes in *Jingle Bells*, joined together by a single line (called a **beam**) in twos or fours - (♫) or (♬) .

These notes are called **quavers** (or **eighth-notes**). You play two of them to each (♩) beat, and the best way to count them is to think of '1 and 2 and' etc.

Clap the rhythm of *Jingle Bells* while you say '1 and 2' - 3 and 4 - , 1 and 2 and 3 - (rest),
1 and 2 and 3 and 4 and , 1 and 2 and 3 - 4 - *etc.*

ACTION REPLAY

Action Replay Instructions. Play these few notes from the tune *slowly* to start with. Then, as your fingers get used to playing them, *repeat them* until you can play them really easily. Finally, *gradually* play them faster until you reach the right speed.

RHYTHM PRACTICE

Clap the rhythms of the the following exercises before you play them:

Now play some of the same rhythms using some of the other notes you have learnt.

Try playing your C scale using some (♪♪) rhythms:

NOTE RECOGNITION GAME

Get a friend to time you as you:

1. **Name** the notes.
2. Say which **valves** you would use.
3. **Play** them.

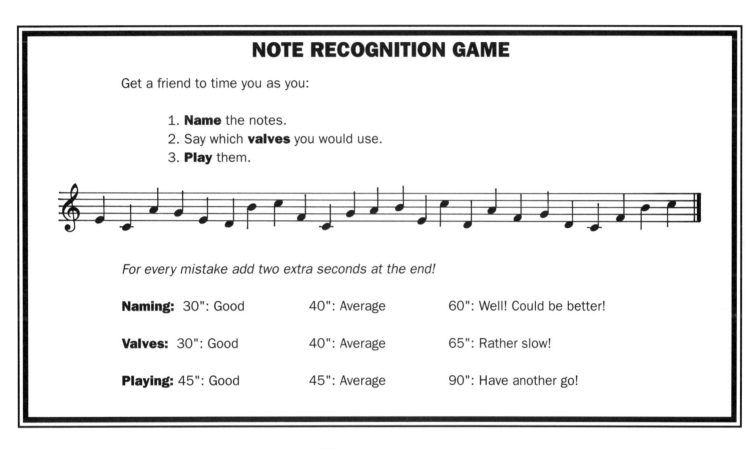

For every mistake add two extra seconds at the end!

Naming:	30": Good	40": Average	60": Well! Could be better!
Valves:	30": Good	40": Average	65": Rather slow!
Playing:	45": Good	45": Average	90": Have another go!

Now try some more tunes which use (♪♪) s.

JOLLY OLD SAINT NICHOLAS

American traditional

ACTION REPLAY

22

KUM-BA-YAH

African traditional

GERMAN STUDENTS' SONG

German students' song

ACTION REPLAY

The last tune was used by the great composer Johannes Brahms (1833-1897) in his *Academic Festival Overture*. Try to hear a recording of this sometime.

HONEY SPREAD ON BROWN, BROWN BREAD

Johannes Brahms (1833-1897)

It is quite likely that you will not know the next tune, but it's a good 'trumpetty' one - see how well you can read it:

A TRUMPET MINUET

English 18th Century

8

ACTION REPLAY

And some more tunes to sight read:

LOOK HERE

B.W.

9

FOLLOW ME

B.W.

10

Here is a tune and a study in ($\frac{2}{4}$) time. There is little difference between two bars of ($\frac{2}{4}$) and one bar of ($\frac{4}{4}$) : in ($\frac{2}{4}$) the beat is **1**, **2** and the accent is 'strong-weak'. Note the repeat in *Jack O' Lantern*.

JACK O'LANTERN

English traditional

SEE THE LIGHT

B.W.

Now learn the duet, *Kookaburra*. Practise both parts, then ask a friend or your teacher to play with you - swap parts!

KOOKABURRA

Traditional

Presumably you noticed that both parts contained the same tune! A piece of music like this is called a **round**.

THREE LITTLE FANFARES

A **Fanfare** is a trumpet call which is played to draw attention to some special event or ceremony.
It must be played *boldly*. A fanfare is sometimes called a 'flourish', and Shakespeare often calls the
ones in his plays, 'sennets'.

These ones might be useful at school!

FANFARE FOR ASSEMBLY

B.W.

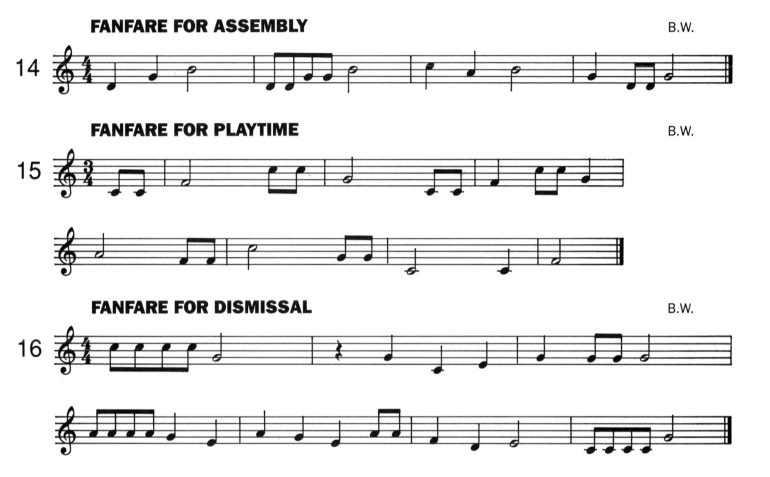

FANFARE FOR PLAYTIME

B.W.

FANFARE FOR DISMISSAL

B.W.

CHECKPOINT

Are you still remembering the advice and instructions on page 14? Turn back and
make sure, before moving on to Stage 6.

STAGE 6

Let's play around with a familiar tune:

ORANGES & LEMONS

English traditional

Oran - ges   and   Le - mons,   say   the   bells   of   St.   Cle - ments

Now try it again, starting on a different note:

Did that sound right?

Play it again and listen carefully - see if you can spot a *wrong note*.

The first note in Bar 3 sounds odd, doesn't it? We need a slightly lower note, half way between **B** and **A**! - this is called **B flat**, and is written on the B line with (♭) in front of it. The **flat** sign (♭) *lowers* a note a little.

B flat (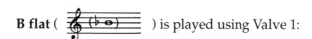) is played using Valve 1:

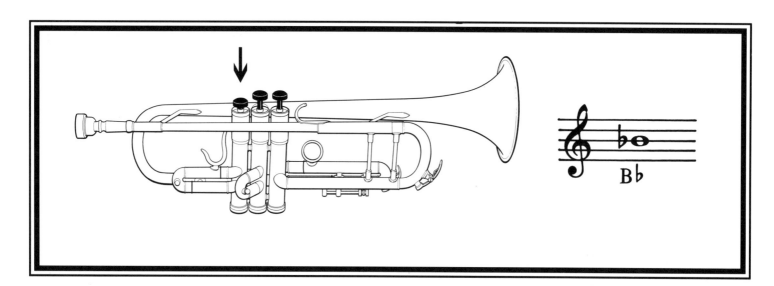

Try the tune again and hear how much better it sounds with B♭ :

Here are some more tunes using this new note:

SUR LE PONT D'AVIGNON — French traditional

MATCHMAKER (FROM FIDDLER ON THE ROOF) — Jerry Bock

O NO, JOHN — Somerset Folk Song

In the next tune some bars contain more than one **B♭**. In each case only the first **B** in the bar has a (♭) sign. Once a (♭) is introduced into a bar *the note remains flat until the next barline.* So, *all* the **B**s in this piece are flat:

YES, PLEASE! — B.W.

STAGE 7

Do you remember the "game" we played at the beginning of Stage 6? Try starting on A:

Now it's the **F** which sounds wrong: this time we need a slightly higher note, half way between **F** and **G**! - it is called **F sharp**, and is written on the F line with (♯) in front of it. The sharp sign (♯) *raises* the note a little.

F sharp () is played using Valve 2:

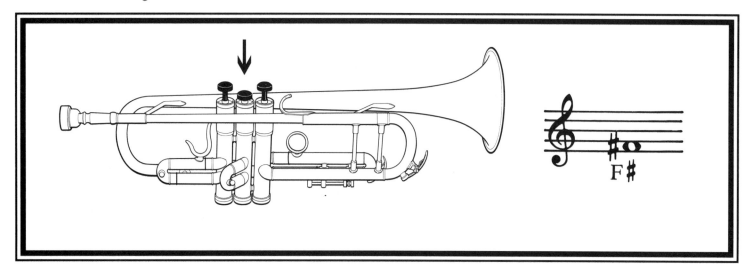

Play Oranges and Lemons using F sharps and it will sound fine:

Now for some other tunes with F sharps:

WHENCE, O SHEPHERD MAIDEN

Canadian traditional

1

ACTION REPLAY

MINI-MARCH

B.W.

Sharps work in just the same way as flats: a (♯) in front of an F makes any Fs following in the same bar **F sharp** as well. Remember this as you play the next two tunes:

GERMAN DANCE NO.6

L. van Beethoven (1770 - 1827)

ACTION REPLAY

MAJESTIC MINUET

B.W.

A note without a flat or sharp is called a **natural**, so most of the notes you have learnt so far are naturals.

(♭) and ♯ signs remain in force *until the next bar line*. So if a tune needs, say, two or more F♯ s in the *same* bar, only the first F is given the ♯ sign - the others are then automatically (♯) .

However, if you need to go back to playing a natural note in the *same* bar as a flat or sharp, the flat or sharp has to be cancelled by using a natural sign (♮).

(♮) is sometimes also used in a following bar simply as a *reminder*, if you have just been playing flats or sharps.

All these signs (♭ , ♯ and ♮) are called **accidentals**.

Try the following exercises. Before you play, think carefully and decide which notes will be flat, sharp or natural:

TO BE OR NOT TO BE
B.W.

SHARPSHOOTER
B.W.

And some more tunes with accidentals - keep your wits about you!:

CHANGING THE GUARD
B.W.

GO DOWN MOSES
American spiritual

THE COVENTRY CAROL
Anon. (English 1591)

TWO'S COMPANY

B.W.

NOTE RECOGNITION GAME

Once again ask someone to time you as you **name** the notes, say which **valves** to use , and finally **play** the notes. Don't forget - 2" extra for any mistake!.

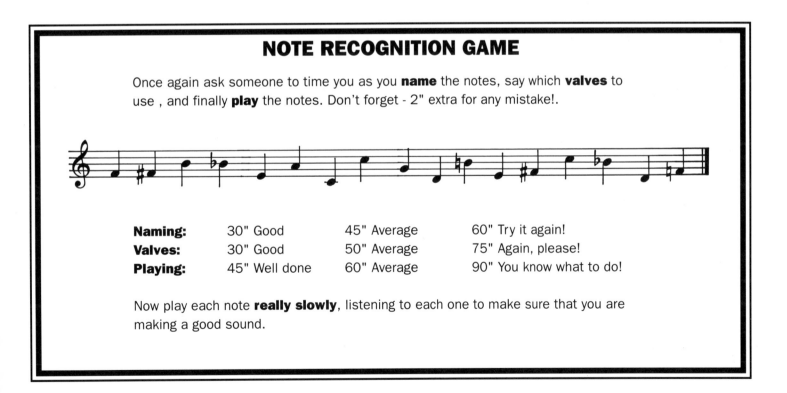

Naming:	30" Good	45" Average	60" Try it again!
Valves:	30" Good	50" Average	75" Again, please!
Playing:	45" Well done	60" Average	90" You know what to do!

Now play each note **really slowly**, listening to each one to make sure that you are making a good sound.

STAGE 8

As the notes you have learnt will now be good and strong, it is time to widen your 'register' (the range of notes that you can play) with notes above and below the two **C**s.

A small step up from  is **C sharp** ( ):

It is played with Valves 1 and 2:

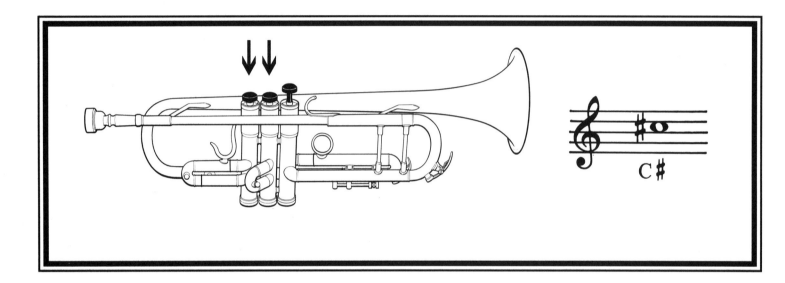

Remember - for the higher notes, draw your lips together *without pressing the mouthpiece hard against them*. Don't force these higher notes - if you *do* find them difficult to produce, keep practising the notes you can play comfortably, and let the high notes develop gradually.

You now know three notes which need Valves 1 & 2 together. Play the following, keeping the two valves down all the time - remember that holding long notes strengthens your playing, so count carefully and give these (**o**) s their full value.

The next tune will give you plenty of practice for the new C♯ :

ROCKING CHAIR SONG

Now, a little higher, to another **D**:

This is played with Valve 1 only:

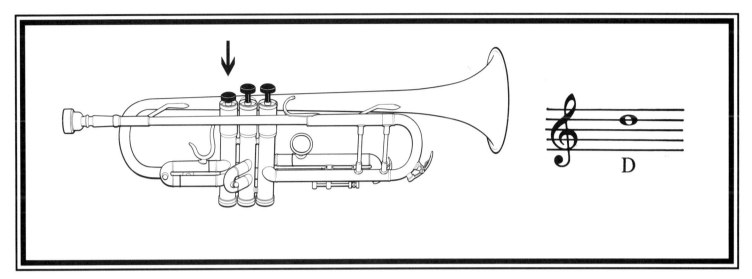

Move up to this new **D**:

Three notes with Valve 1 - keep it pressed down as you play:

Now some tunes using these two new notes;

FIGHT THE GOOD FIGHT

J. Hatton (d. 1793)

SONG OF THE VOLGA BOATMEN

Russian traditional

ANNIE'S SONG

John Denver

Count carefully on the long tied notes.

HELSTON FLORAL DANCE

Cornish traditional

Note that both sections of this tune are repeated. At the end of the second section you go back to

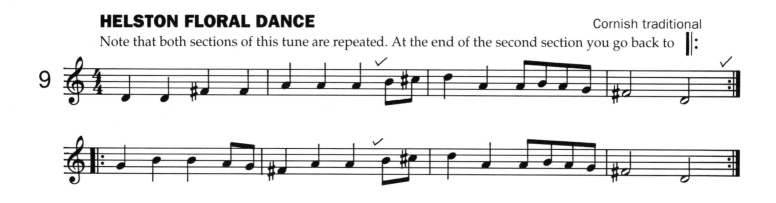

QUELLE EST CETTE ODEUR AGRÉABLE

French traditional carol

D.C. is short for *Da Capo*, Italian for "to the head", i.e. *go back to the beginning*. *Fine* means *"finish here"*.

ON PARADE

B.W.

SWINGS AND ROUNDABOUTS

B.W.

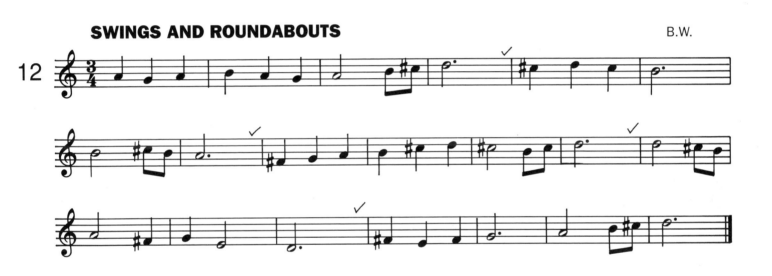

STAGE 9

Now for some *low* notes.

If you play 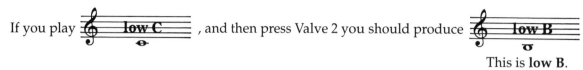 , and then press Valve 2 you should produce

This is **low B**.

Try it!

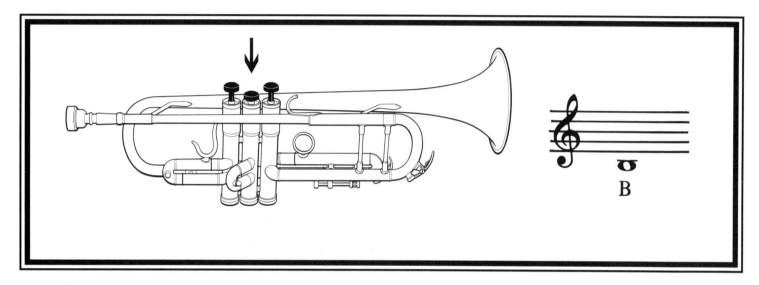

Remember to relax your lip a little and, as you go down, bring your lower jaw slightly forward.

Now another step down to **low B♭** . This note is played with Valve 1.

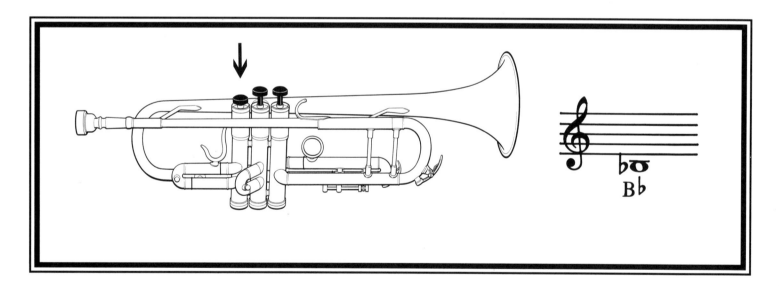

Try this little exercise. See if you can produce really 'fat' notes:

And here is an exercise playing all the notes you know with Valve 2, followed by those with Valve 1:

Now for some tunes in the low register:

POOR WAYFARING STRANGER

American traditional

MORNING HAS BROKEN

Gaelic traditional

FINNISH FOLK TUNE

Anon (Finnish 17th Century)

MELODY IN F

Anton Rubinstein (1829-1894)

And some low tunes for sight-reading:

IN SOMBRE MOOD
B.W.

BELOW STAIRS
B.W.

BASEMENT BLUES
B.W.

NIGHT WATCH
B.W.

CHECKPOINT

Do remember to relax your lip as you descend to these lower regions. Don't blow too hard down there - breathe *gently* into the tube. Remember to use a little more lower lip - bring your bottom jaw *forward* a little.

STAGE 10

SLURS

Up to now you have been trying to tongue very hard, so that the start of each note is clean and immediately responsive.

However, there are times when you need to move from one note to another smoothly. We call this **slurring**: the musical term for this is called playing **legato**.

To slur on the trumpet you tongue the first note and then *change to another note while continuing to keep the air moving through the tube.*

Try these four little exercises:

Remember to *keep blowing* as you change the valves *quickly*.

Now here are some tunes that you may have heard - they all have slurs:

AURA LEE

ACTION REPLAY

WE THREE KINGS

J.H. Hopkins (19th Century)

6

AMAZING GRACE

Scottish traditional

7

THE BRITISH GRENADIERS

English traditional

8

ACTION REPLAY

AIR FROM THE PEASANT CANTATA

J.S. Bach (1685-1750)

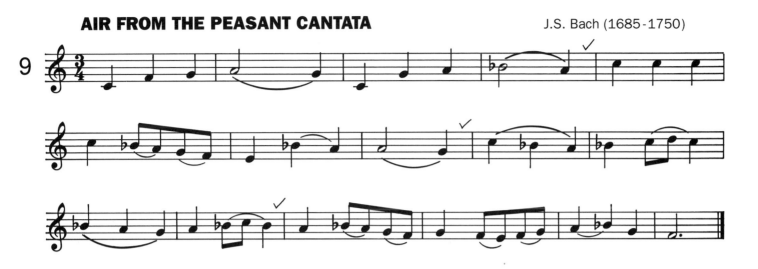

Four tunes for slurring and sight-reading practice:

GLIDING

B.W.

SAILING

B.W.

SKATING

B.W.

12

ROLLING

B.W.

13

ACTION REPLAY

How about turning back and playing some of the earlier tunes, *adding slurs where you think they will sound good?*

STAGE 11

DOTTED CROTCHET (QUARTER-NOTE) RHYTHMS

Here are the first few bars of *God Save The Queen* (Americans know this tune as *My Country, 'tis of Thee*):

English 18th Century

1

What do you notice that is different in this tune?

In two places there are (♩) s with dots after them, followed by (♪) s. A (♪) is a *single* quaver (eighth-note).

RHYTHM PRACTICE

Here are some exercises to get you used to playing (♩. ♪).
Count **1** (2) **and** 3 (4) in the first one - you'll soon get the idea:

Now some tunes using this new rhythm:

STEAL AWAY
American spiritual

SCARBOROUGH FAIR
English traditional

WORRIED MAN BLUES

American traditional

MINKA

Russian Folk Song

THE HARP THAT ONCE THROUGH TARA'S HALLS

Irish traditional

Can you remember all the notes you have learnt? Put yourself to the test!...

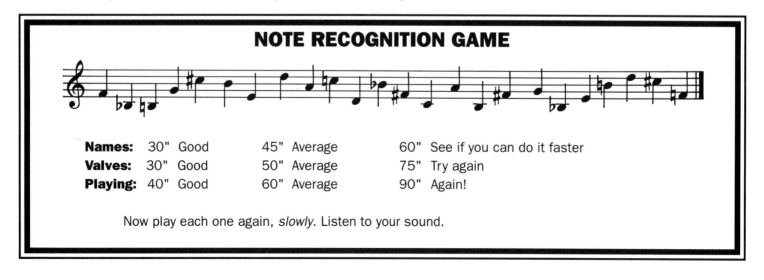

NOTE RECOGNITION GAME

Names:	30" Good	45" Average	60" See if you can do it faster
Valves:	30" Good	50" Average	75" Try again
Playing:	40" Good	60" Average	90" Again!

Now play each one again, *slowly*. Listen to your sound.

Now for some less familiar tunes:

BOLD GRENADIER

B.W.

At the beginning of Stage 6 we had a game playing the same tune in different keys. Let's do the same with some more tunes:

JOHNNY TODD IN C

English traditional

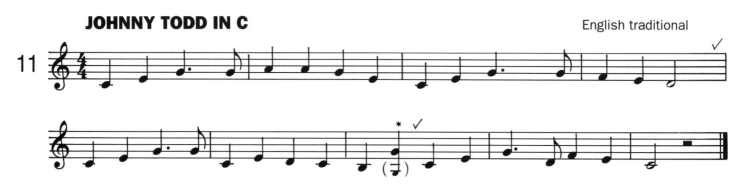

*There are two notes together here. The bracketed one is how the tune is usually played, but as this note is not familiar, it is better if you play the higher one for the moment.

Here is *Johnny Todd* in the key of **F**:

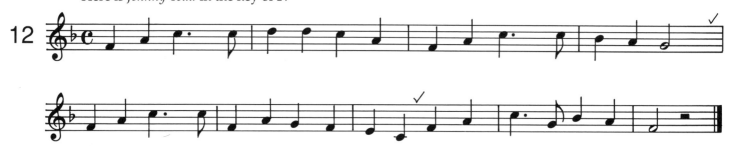

Although we need a **B♭**, you will have noticed that it is not written in. But if you look carefully at the beginning of each line you will see a ♭ on the **B** line. This is called the **key signature**. It tells you that every time you see a **B** you must play **B♭**.

Here is the start of another famous tune which has its origin in one of Josef Haydn's string quartets. It is well known both as the German National Anthem, *Deutschland über alles,* and as the hymn tune 'Austria', sung to the words *Glorious things of Thee are spoken*. First it is in the key of C:

AUSTRIA

Josef Haydn (1732 - 1809)

Now try it in the key of F:

Did you get the **B**(♭)s?

And in the key of **D**. The key-signature of 2 ♯s tells you to play every **F** and every **C** as sharps. Before you play, identify these **F**s and **C**s. The **low C♯** is a new note, which will be dealt with thoroughly in Book 2. It is played with all three valves. Have a go:

The group of notes in brackets [ ] is a good valve exercise for the 3rd finger, which has a tendency to be weak. Practise the following few bars:

Now try *God save the Queen* in the same three keys:

GOD SAVE THE QUEEN

STAGE 12

SYNCOPATION

Here are two well-known tunes for you:

OLD MAN RIVER

Jerome Kern (1885-1945)

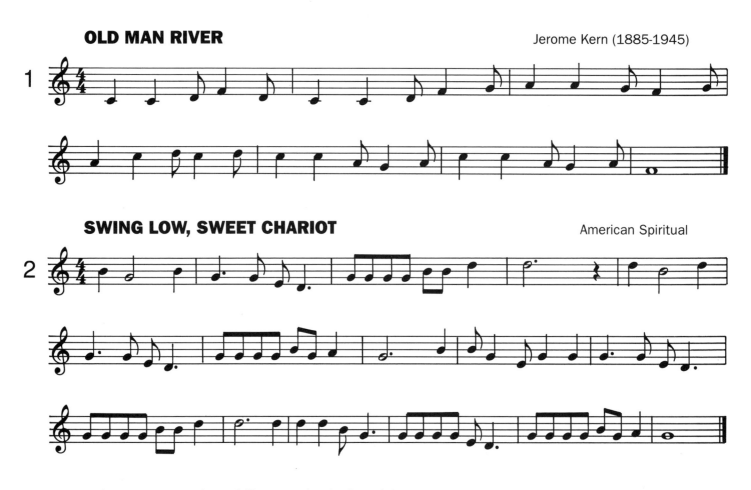

SWING LOW, SWEET CHARIOT

American Spiritual

Did you notice anything different in the rhythm of these two tunes?

If not, try them again and look, count and listen carefully.

At times the short note (♪) comes *on* the beat and the longer, stronger one (♩) or (♩.) is played half-way through a beat. We call this **syncopation**. This rhythm is used a lot in popular music.

Here are some more tunes with syncopation:

THE LONG AND WINDING ROAD

Lennon & McCartney

SHORT'NIN' BREAD

American traditional

COCKLES & MUSSELS

Irish traditional

GOING TO THE ZOO

Tom Paxton

Syncopation Practice:

1   2   3   & (4) &

1   2 & (3 4)

1 & (2) 3 & 4

1 & (2) 3 & (4) &   1 2 3 & (4)

You could put some syncopation into your **C** scale, e.g.:

Have a go at this Jamaican song, which you may have heard before - it is usually called *Mango Walk*, although sometimes known as *Jamaican Rhumba*.

MANGO WALK

Jamaican traditional

9

And some more sight-reading practice:

SYNTHETIC SPIRITUAL

B.W.

10

JAZZY WALTZ

B.W.

11

SCALES

By now you will be able to play the C scale from memory. As you play, *listen to the distance that you go from one note to the next*.

Scales are made up of steps: if you listen really carefully, you will notice that two of these steps (between notes 3 & 4 and between notes 7 & 8) are shorter than others.

In keys other than C we use sharps and flats to make sure that the short steps come in the right places. Try D:

All the notes of the scale of B♭ will be familiar to you except the fourth one, E♭ - you play this with Valves 2 and 3:

You might like to try this different kind of scale:

It is called a **minor scale** - all the ones you've played so far are known as **major scales**. When you come down, you will notice that two of the notes are changed. It also sounds rather sad. Compare it with the **D major** scale.

By now the notes and tunes in this book should be quite easy for you, so let's move on to Book 2, higher and lower notes and new rhythms so that you'll be able to play even better tunes!

Perhaps you will be able to join a band or even an orchestra!

Above all, *ENJOY* YOUR TRUMPET PLAYING.

FINGERING CHART

Here, for easy reference, are all the notes that you have learnt in this book.
The Contents page tells you where the notes were first introduced and where to
find tunes to practise using them.